THE FIGHT

Copyright © 2021 by Dr. Brittany Patterson
ISBN: 978-1-7376938-9-5
Library of Congress Control Number: 2021917867
Published in Austin, Texas
All rights reserved. No part of this publication may be reproduced, distributed, or transmitted in any form or by any means, including photocopying, recording, or other electronic or mechanical methods, without the prior written permission of the publisher or author, except in the case of brief quotations embodied in critical reviews and certain other noncommercial uses permitted by copyright law.
Although every precaution has been taken to verify the accuracy of the information contained herein, the author and publisher assume no responsibility for any errors or omissions. No liability is assumed for damages that may result from the use of information contained within.

—105—
PUBLISHING
EST. 2020

Dedication

The Fight is dedicated to all students, including my own

children –

You deserve safe spaces to learn and grow,

full of opportunities to share what you know,

and elevation of your talents for obstacles foreseen,

ensuring accomplishment of every goal and unseen dream.

- Dr. Brittany Patterson (2020)

The Fight

Written by:

Dr. Brittany Patterson

Illustrated by:

Shelly Lipscomb

Introduction

The purpose of *The Fight* is to encourage conversation about important skills needed to handle problems in a helpful way. To benefit most from this book, respond to each reflection question in the order presented and as honestly as possible. There are no right or wrong answers, but thinking through them will help with understanding key messages from the story. Start with the "Warm-Up" and then begin reading *The Fight*. After finishing the story, complete the "Cool-Down" and consider sharing your response to the final question with the author.

Warm-Up

1. What does it mean to fight?

2. What does it mean to feel powerless?

3. What does it mean to feel powerful?

4. What skills do you use to handle difficult situations in a helpful way?

Hurt by the sting of another kid's words, your peers exchange whispers and gather in herds.

Situations like this happen often in life, yet these are experiences most do not like.

Whether mean or unfair, it doesn't seem right. And though not rare, it's hard to handle quite right.

How would you feel if you were insulted in front of other people?

You start to feel embarrassed about the blatant disrespect, growing confused and upset – even fuming as you reflect.

"I'm the target of all mean jokes! Why? What did I do?"
Or, "Why are you talking about me when I didn't say anything
to you?"

With clenched fists and puffed up cheeks,
your heart races and you begin to reach your peak.

You growl aloud as a thought takes over your mind.
"I'm done dealing with this!" and there is only one option,
you've resigned.

What types of thoughts would go through your mind if you were in this situation?

Now it's time to battle, and your decision really matters.

Which direction is for you?

Select door one, or choose door number two.

What would you do next? Do you think your decision would lead you through the Powerless or Powerful door?

Ready to duke it out with the person of the day?

No matter what they say or what they do,
if you make this choice,
it's a Powerless fight for you.

Head down this route, it's your right to choose.
But be forewarned, the ensuing fight will be against you.

Immediately jumping in and fighting with no fears,
you swing at moving targets every time a problem appears.

**What does it mean to fight against yourself? How
have you fought against yourself in the past?**

You might feel better for a moment, that is, until the consequences appear.

Discipline referral.
Detention.
Parent-teacher conference.
Out-of-school suspension.

Every incident is a "mistake" and "won't happen again," or "It's their fault, why didn't you catch them?"

Powerless fighting, pleading, and blaming on repeat, never noticing it's your academics, friendships, and spirit you defeat.

Describe a consequence that made you feel powerless in the past? What about that consequence made you feel powerless?

Eventually, your response pattern becomes clear.
Now, it's only a short time before the next challenger appears.

Struggling alone, you find the Powerless fight a lonely one,
with no end in sight and no trophy to be won.

And as you continue to fight day in and day out,
eventually you give in to self-inflicted doubt.

"There's nothing I can do."
"Things won't improve."
"Why even try because I'll only lose."

What negative thoughts have you had about yourself?
How did they affect you?

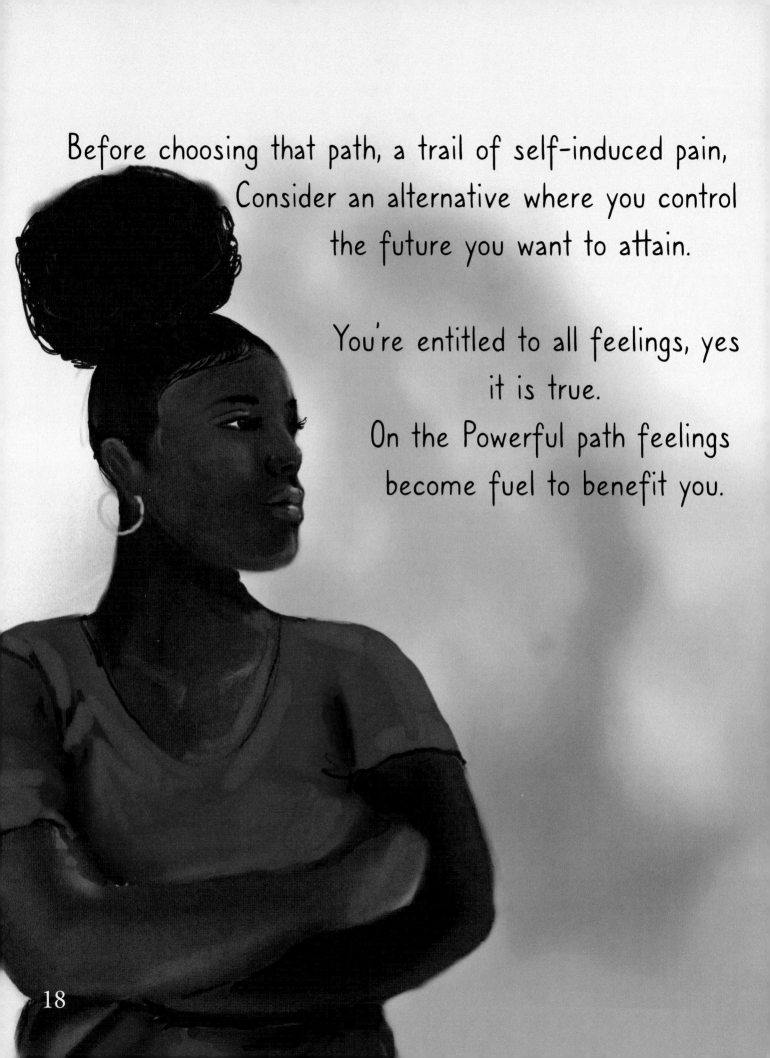

Before choosing that path, a trail of self-induced pain,
Consider an alternative where you control
the future you want to attain.

You're entitled to all feelings, yes
it is true.
On the Powerful path feelings
become fuel to benefit you.

This is the direction for those with eyes set toward success, where fighting involves thoughtful decision-making to cope with the stress.

So what can you do about the event that bothered you? Choose one or more FIGHT skills to help get you through.

How would you describe the Powerless fight? What do you think will be different about the Powerful fight?

Address strong FEELINGS that can narrow your view. You can't allow emotions to dictate your behavior and what happens to you.

Now breathe to open your sight and then breathe deeply once again.
Gaining control of the situation begins with calming the environment within.

What helps you to calm down when you experience strong feelings?

Discover the strengths of your IDENTITY and take stock of qualities that make you unique.
Then count the places, people, and things you value. See them each as a puzzle piece.

Evaluate your strengths and resources to creatively fit them together.
Chances are you have most of what you need to handle this and any stressor.

What personal strengths can you use to overcome challenging situations? What additional resources can help you deal with the problems you will face?

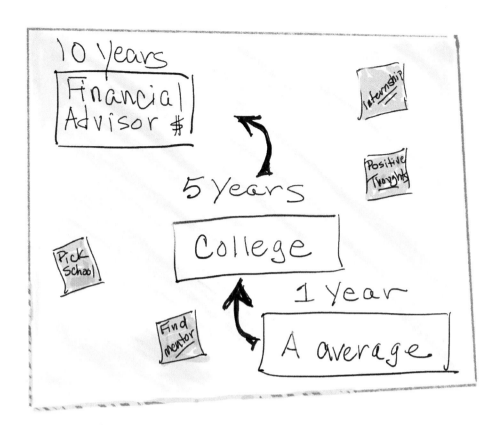

Focus on personal GOALS as you consider options available to you.

Start by asking, "Who do I want to be in the future?" or "What achievements do I want to move closer to?"

Allow your goals to serve as a map when you face a difficult situation.

They will guide you away from wrong turns and toward the desired destination.

What personal goal are you most motivated to achieve?
Why is this goal so important to you?

HEALTHY COPING is the skill that will move you beyond simply surviving.
Practice incorporating things important to you and soon you'll be thriving.

So walk away and hit the court. Intense energy can push you to new limits.
Channel anger into your sport and notice the relief you feel after just a few minutes.

Or speak to a trusted person about the pressure of emotions brewing within,
then gain their perspective. Ask, "What would you do?" or, "What direction would you go in?"

Try putting emotions into dance, painting, music, or poetry. You'll start to feel better.
Art is a healthy outlet that produces creations you and others will treasure.

31

Or, choose to advocate for what is right and speak up
with a purpose.
There is power in protest and groups fighting as a
united force.

Many positive outcomes can result from
feelings of frustration,
as such strong emotions carry the energy
required to change a nation.

How would you define healthy coping? What does healthy coping look like for you?

Finally, the Powerful fight requires THOUGHTS of self-love, confidence, encouragement, and persistence, to battle the unfair insults, doubts, discouragement, and resistance.

Command your mind to see the best in you. Say:

Each claim is 100% true, and winning is the only option when you see yourself as unbreakable.

Give an example of a thought that makes you feel strong, confident, or powerful.

Now that you know,
the Powerless fight is an illusion
of strength and bravery,
that over time creates
weakness and
emotional slavery.

Now that you
know,
the Powerful fight
is a commitment
to what you want to
accomplish,
that will always allow you to
learn, grow, and flourish.

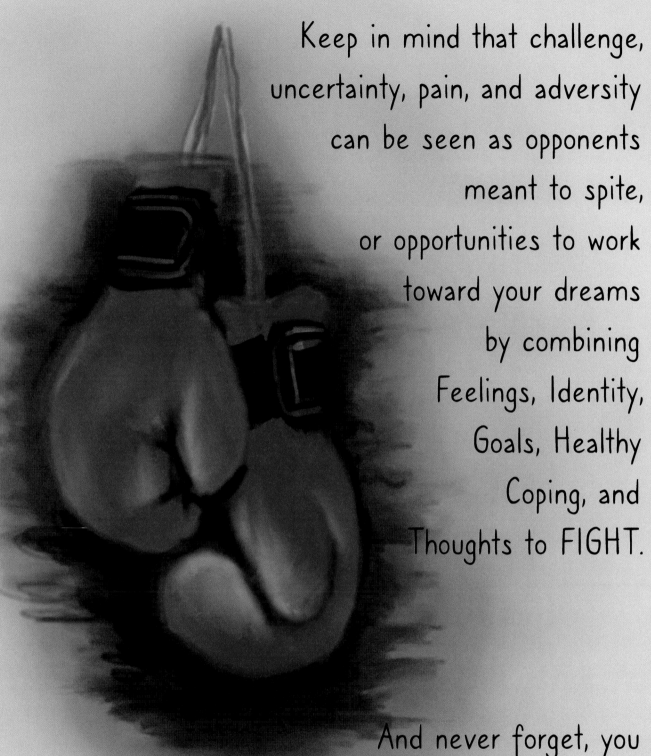

Keep in mind that challenge,
uncertainty, pain, and adversity
can be seen as opponents
meant to spite,
or opportunities to work
toward your dreams
by combining
Feelings, Identity,
Goals, Healthy
Coping, and
Thoughts to FIGHT.

And never forget, you
always have control over
whether you win or lose,
because how you fight is a decision only you can choose.

For once again a time will come that you must step into the ring.

Which fight will you choose? Ding! Ding!

What are the main differences between the Powerless and Powerful fights?
If you were the main character, which fight would you choose and why?

39

Cool-Down

1. What does it mean to fight?

2. What does it mean to feel powerless?

3. What does it mean to feel powerful?

4. When faced with a difficult situation, it's important to focus on 1) Feelings, 2) Identity, 3) Goals, 4) Healthy Coping, and 5) Thoughts -- the FIGHT skills. Which FIGHT skill(s) do you already use to help you overcome challenging situations? Which FIGHT skills do you need to practice?

5. Use original writing, drawing, painting, poetry, or music to demonstrate how you can use the FIGHT skills to overcome difficult situations. Submit your responses to the author at drbrittpatterson@gmail.com for a chance to be featured on The Fight Facebook and Instagram pages. In the email, include your first name, age, city, and state.

About the Author

Brittany R. Patterson, Ph.D. obtained her bachelor's degree in Psychology from St. Lawrence University and doctorate in School/Counseling Psychology from The University at Buffalo. Currently, Dr. Patterson is a licensed Psychologist and Assistant Professor at the University of Maryland School of Medicine (UMSOM). She has worked in schools for more than a decade in various capacities and specializes in providing  high-quality school-based mental health services in traditionally underserved educational settings. Dr. Patterson is particularly passionate about identifying and building upon the strengths of youth and their communities to promote positive mental health and well-being. In fact, *The Fight* was inspired by five years of serving a Title I school in Baltimore City where she was consistently impressed by the gifts and talents of our "fighters"—students often in trouble for behavioral or emotional needs. She found that invested adults, dedicated time, and ample skill building opportunities made a significant difference for the "fighters" and enabled many to not only survive but thrive!

Beyond her professional dedication to schools, Dr. Patterson is a proud daughter, sister, wife, and mother. Her hobbies include spending time with her family over food, arts, crafts, outdoor sports, and reading.

105 Publishing LLC
www.105publishing.com
Austin, Texas

Made in the USA
Monee, IL
20 October 2021

80051480R00026